High Adventure

the days of
DAVY CROCKETT

By Clive Hopwood
Illustrated by Glenn Rix

Snow lay thick upon the ground and hung heavily on the branches of the trees as the bobcat wove its sleek, feline way through the undergrowth. On the scent of a young deer, it paused in its silent quest, the sensitive eyes probing through the trees for a sight of its prey. A slight movement, glimpsed between the heavy-laden boughs, and the bobcat edged forward stealthily, muscles superbly poised for instant pursuit.

The deer, seemingly unaware, continued pawing at the ground through the snow, its head bobbing as it scratched out the occasional tasty morsel. The bobcat, a quiet and secretive animal, is that deadliest of foes, the silent hunter, and in the backwoods neither man nor beast can ever feel sure that the eyes of a bobcat are not following his every move. Sure of itself, the big cat closed in for the kill, its muscular legs powering it through the soft, deep carpet of snow. At the last instant it caught sight of another creature, concealed and waiting, the upright stance bearing the mark of a man.

A single shot rang out and the bobcat dropped in its tracks, the startled deer straining at its leash to flee from the noise.

Davy Crockett stepped into the clearing and surveyed the warm, furred body, a neat hole penetrating its skull behind the ear. Slinging the catch over his shoulder he untied the deer, the bait he had used to lure his prey and, whistling, set off through the trees.

He felt supremely satisfied, the satisfaction of the hunter who knows he has overcome a skilful and worthy adversary. It had been the labour of many days, as time after time the bobcat had sprung his traps and escaped with the carefully laid bait. Davy had enjoyed the contest, the matching of one hunter against another, pitting of patience and cunning against instinct.

Reaching his cabin, Davy tethered the deer securely in an adjoining outhouse and hung the bobcat in a separate compartment ready for skinning later. Alongside it numerous furs and skins of fox, mink, and beaver stood silent witness to Davy's skill as a hunter and trapper. It had been a good winter, his haul of furs from hunting and trapping well past his expectations.

He went into the cabin, stoked the fire up with some wood, and put on some coffee to heat. Outside a faint wind threw flurries of light, powdery snow against the door, and the sky darkened, looking set for another snowfall before the day was out.

A loner by nature, Davy enjoyed the occasional company of his fellow man on his visits to small towns and trading posts, but preferred the vast, uninhabited reaches of the backwoods. Not that to Davy the backwoods were uninhabited. True that few men, except trappers and hunters like himself, ventured into their largely unexplored depths, but the country teemed with wildlife, their infinite variety and character never ceasing to make him wonder.

He finished his coffee, and took up his long rifle and powder horn. He would have time to collect his day's catch from the traps and reset them before the snowstorm closed in. His tall, rangy form filled the small cabin which he had built himself only as a place to sleep, eat and take shelter in between hunting. Outside was all the space he needed. Like the animals he hunted, he saw home as a haven from storms, a refuge to return to, and nothing more.

He opened the door and stepped out into the bracing air. He was about to start off when the distant sound of human voices, away to his left, caught his attention. To hear a human voice was a strange enough occurrence in itself, but these sounded threatening. He cocked his ear and listened. If he were not mistaken these were Indians on the hunt, and by the noise they were making their prey was human rather than animal.

He began a slow trot towards the receding shouts, and presently he heard them change direction towards him. Their quarry, whoever it might be, was obviously endeavouring to make towards the river, which lay some half mile beyond Davy's cabin. Perhaps the fugitive hoped to swim to safety through the deep, swirling waters that characterised the river in these parts. It would certainly be the act of a desperate man, for the currents were swift and dangerous at this point, but from the shouts and yelps Davy was in no doubt that this party of Indians were not tracking their man, but had him in sight and were in full pursuit. Davy reckoned them to be less than a mile distant, and closing fast.

The noise drew nearer and Davy instinctively sought cover until he could know the strength of the opposition. He had barely hidden himself behind some trees on the edge of a clearing when the figure of a young Choctaw Indian burst through the undergrowth on the opposite side. His face looked pained and exhausted, partly from the running, partly from a vicious wound that caused his left leg to drag. It was obvious that he could not avoid capture and probable death for much longer.

As chance would have it, the Indian headed unknowingly straight for where Davy stood hiding. As he passed within inches Davy reached out and pulled him in beside him, then raised his long rifle ready to meet the oncoming pursuers. The young Indian, whether from exhaustion or surrender, remained where he was, uncertain but uncaring who his saviour was.

Almost at once a figure entered the clearing in full flight but slowed to regain his bearings. At that moment Davy pulled the trigger and the Indian twisted upwards with the impact of the shot, collapsing to a lifeless heap on the floor. Two more figures had appeared hard on his heels, but stopped dead, and then raced back for the trees seeing their fallen companion.

An unearthly silence filled the clearing. Snow began to fall, slowly at first and then more thickly, until the air

was virtually opaque with white blots. Minutes passed, and Davy, accustomed to the slow, patient stance of the hunter, stood his ground, motioning the Indian beside him to be still. The Indian needed no second bidding; he too knew the laws of the hunter.

After some considerable length of time, discerning no movement, the hunting party obviously decided it was at last safe to venture forward. Davy, having reloaded, allowed them to advance almost as far as the prostrate body before unleashing a second deadly volley. The remainder fled into the trees within seconds.

"It'll be safe now," whispered Davy. "They won't dare come out into the open again. They'll circle slowly round the clearing to try and come up back of us—but we'll be long gone. Come on."

Helping the young Indian up, Davy painstakingly withdrew from their position, eyes and ears alert for any possible attack. There was none. Before long, however, it became evident that his companion—week and ill-clad for such severe weather—was close to dropping. Davy bent and slung him across his shoulder like a carcass, the indian too feeble to protest, and proceeded to carry him.

It was almost half an hour before Davy and his burden gained the shelter of the cabin. It was a hard haul and Davy felt the relief flood into his body as he laid the now unconscious Indian on the floor beside the stove. He stooped and put an ear to the injured man's chest. He was still breathing at least. Despite the cold, blood was oozing from the wound on his thigh, which was obviously in need of immediate attention.

Davy carried the limp figure to the bed, and made the necessary preparations to attend to the wound, which from all appearances was the type delivered by a tomahawk blow. The Indian remained mercifully unconscious and Davy set to work.

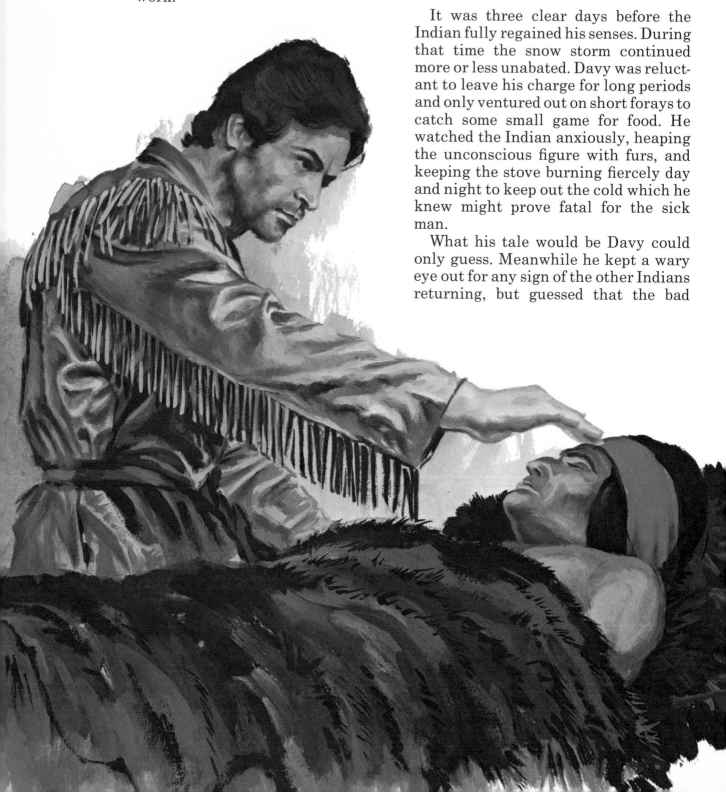

It was three clear days before the Indian fully regained his senses. During that time the snow storm continued more or less unabated. Davy was reluctant to leave his charge for long periods and only ventured out on short forays to catch some small game for food. He watched the Indian anxiously, heaping the unconscious figure with furs, and keeping the stove burning fiercely day and night to keep out the cold which he knew might prove fatal for the sick man.

What his tale would be Davy could only guess. Meanwhile he kept a wary eye out for any sign of the other Indians returning, but guessed that the bad

weather had fortunately intervened to dissuade them from further pursuit.

At last, over a period of some hours, the wounded Indian regained consciousness. He drifted in and out of a semi-dreamlike state like waves beating upon a shore, his mind obviously troubled by the events leading up to his rescue. When finally he seemed to register where he was, the brave slowly found his memory of Davy coming back to him and could not thank him enough for saving his life. Davy calmed him, handed him a bowl of thick, meaty rabbit stew, and sat down beside him on the makeshift bed.

"You are a Choctaw," said Davy, speaking in the Indian's own tongue. The Indian nodded, surprised to hear his own language spoken by so unfamiliar a figure. Davy smiled. "I know your people well. Many times I have taken food and smoked the pipe of peace with your great chiefs."

The Indian seemed reassured, and continued consuming the stew with a ravenous appetite that spoke of many days without food.

"Those braves who pursued you," continued Davy, "they are not of your tribe. What caused them to pursue you like a hunted animal?"

The Indian wiped up the last smear of gravy with his fingers and set the bowl on the floor. He seemed to feel much better for the food. He raised himself stiffly on one elbow.

"They are a renegade band of the Wichita tribe, my white brother."

"But I had not heard that Choctaw and Wichita were at war," replied Davy. "Surely these are peaceful peoples who lives their lives in harmony together?"

The brave shook his head. "I will tell you a tale, white brother, of much grief and many deaths." Davy handed the Indian a cup of hot coffee and sat back to listen.

"One moon past, I and several braves from my tribe were on a hunting trip to collect food for my village. It has been a hard winter and we were forced to go far in our search." Davy nodded, understanding. "One day we were camped by the great river when this band of Wichita braves descended upon us, slaughtering my brothers without mercy. I alone escaped, and for many days they have followed me, fearful no doubt that I should return to my people and tell of this treachery."

The Indian paused to take a sip from the steaming cup.

"Well, at least you've lived to tell the tale," said Davy.

"And to seek vengeance for my dead brothers," returned the Indian.

"Not just yet," answered Davy, beginning to unwrap the bandage around the Indian's leg. "This wound is going to take a while to heal. You'll be in no fit state to go on the warpath for a month or two, I'd say. The leg needs rest first, and then to be gradually brought back into use. Hurry this and you could have a limp for the rest of your life."

The Indian smiled. "You speak wisely, white brother. I am hot-headed, impatient to hunt down my enemy—but like the hunter I must wait until I am ready, concentrate all my energies onto my prey, and let the Great Spirits guide me to him when the time is right." He looked down at the cleaned wound approvingly. "You make good medicine and save my life—but what should I call you, white brother?"

"Davy Crockett's my name."

"Davy Crockett," repeated the Indian. "I will remember you. Mine is White Eagle. Good. Now we are friends."

For the remainder of the winter Davy and White Eagle lived together. Once he was able to walk again, White Eagle would accompany Davy on his hunting and trapping trips, and the two men taught each other much of their different ways. A warm friendship developed between them, such as Davy had not known for many years. Indeed, when spring came and White Eagle announced he must return to his people, Davy was sad to see him go.

"Fear not, Davy," said White Eagle, as they parted one fine April morning. "Just as the raindrops are separated when they fall from the sky, so they will be reunited when they both flow into the great river. We too shall meet again some day, my brother."

The same day White Eagle left, Davy loaded his impressive collection of skins and furs into his canoe, which he kept concealed a short distance from the river bank. The journey down river to Natchez was uneventful, and Davy found himself looking forward to meeting the townspeople. They had always struck him as friendly folk, yet this time the loss of the companionable White Eagle made him all the more eager to indulge in a little socialising.

At that time of year Natchez was always full of travellers of one kind or another. Trappers and fur traders descended on the town to buy and sell furs, and Davy came across many friends and acquaintances with whom he spent many an enjoyable evening, drinking and talking over old times, or relating news of recent events. In the absence of any more reliable source of news, word of mouth accounts were passed between travellers when they met, and Davy having seen virtually nobody during his time in the backwoods, was an eager listener.

Davy was talking one day to a trader by the name of Leclerque. He was a Frenchman who dealt in a wide number of goods, including furs, which was how Davy came to know him. Leclerque was widely travelled, and his dealings often took him far afield, visiting Indian settlements far to the north. He had made mention, in passing, of a particularly savage incident related to him by one tribe when their village had been raided by a band of Wichita braves. Recalling White Eagle's story instantly, Davy enquired if the Frenchman had heard any further details of this band.

"*Mais oui, mon ami*," began Leclerque, "everywhere I go I hear these terrible stories. In some places every village has a tale to tell of these murderers."

"And it's always the same band, huh?" asked Davy.

"That is so, Davy," answered Leclerque. "I hear that these are a band of renegade warriors from the Wichita tribe. Their leader, Black Bear, was made an outcast from his people and he left, taking some of the more rebellious young warriors with him. They have become, er . . . the word . . . nomadic, travelling round, raiding villages, murdering, stealing food, weapons, clothes. It is a terrible thing, no?"

"I've heard of them myself," replied Davy, "but until now I didn't know who they were. I didn't *think* the Wichitas were at war."

"*Mais non*, but this band," said the Frenchman, throwing his hands in the air, "they are at war with everyone. But this Black Bear, he is a clever one. They try to catch him, but always he escapes, he is the devil himself. Few are the men who have lived to tell of his treachery. *Mon ami*, I tell you," continued Leclerque, drawing Davy towards him, "I have heard of him killing whole villages of women and children and old men while the braves are away hunting. Ah, an evil man, Davy. I hope we may never meet, may *le bon Dieu* preserve me."

The tale interested Davy greatly and his mind drifted to thoughts of White Eagle. He wondered whether he too had heard these stories when he returned to his village, and how his quest for vengeance was progressing. Doubtless, if such a notorious outlaw were caught, the news would spread far and wide.

The next two or three days Davy was busy buying provisions for his next hunting expedition, and he thought little more about it, although new arrivals to the town brought several varying stories of Black Bear's vile exploits. It wasn't until the morning of his departure that Davy became truly involved in the whole business.

He was stocking up with one or two final oddments for his trip when a man burst in through the door. Old Joe, who ran the store, was known for his rudimentary but sound knowledge of medicine, and folk often came to him for help or advice. Situated at the north end of town, he was frequently the nearest available source of first aid for injured men coming into town from the open country.

"Better come quick, Joe," said the man, hurriedly. "There's a man out here hurt real bad."

"Mind the store, will you, Maisy," clipped Joe, reaching for his hat and coat and, accompanied by Davy, he hurried out to see what was wrong.

A large crowd had already gathered on the opposite side of the street, and Joe and Davy had to push their way through to get to the injured man. A ragged, filthy appearance suggested that he had been travelling on foot for some days, a jagged cut across his forehead and a blood-soaked sleeve testifying to some kind of fight.

The man, while obviously seriously ill, was anxious to pass on his news. Through hollowed eye sockets he focused wearily on Joe and Davy, the breath coming in shallow, rasping gasps while he spoke.

"Wagon train, near Natchitoches," he blurted, "just three wagons . . . heading west. . . ." He paused to catch his breath, coughing a little blood. After

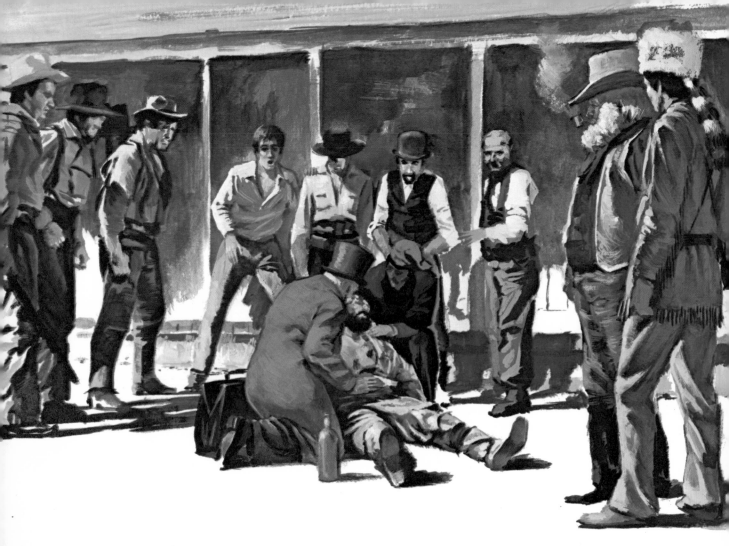

a moment he continued, despite attempts to quieten him. "Indians . . . out of nowhere . . . killed all men . . . took my wife . . . left me for dead . . . escaped . . . you must . . . you must. . . ."

His voice faded to silence as the effort became too much for him and he passed out in Joe's arms.

"Better get him inside, boys," said Joe, and a dozen willing hands bent to pick up the man.

Davy stood up, a thoughtful look on his face. He found Leclerque by his side. It was evident their thoughts were the same.

"It looks like this Black Bear is still at large, *mon ami*," commented Leclerque.

Davy nodded slowly. "I reckon it's about time somebody went out and caught that varmint. Seems to me he's done enough killing and now this woman—"

"You think maybe he keep her alive?"

"Maybe. She is a white woman after all," replied Davy. "Could be he sees her as some kind of prize."

"I do not like the look I see in your eyes, *mon ami*, It says you are thinking that perhaps you are the man who will hunt down this Black Bear."

"Whatever gives you that idea, Frenchie?" grinned Davy. "It just so happens I was thinking of heading up towards Natchitoches anyway. What I hunt for when I get there depends on what I find." Leclerque thought he discerned a slight twinkle in Davy's eyes. "Now, if you'll excuse me, there's a couple of things I still need from the store."

Leclerque watched Davy walk determinedly across the street to the store, and he knew he was right. He had known Davy long enough to recognise that once he had an idea there was no shaking him. Never one to miss an opportunity, he also realised this piece of news would be worth a drink or two from his friends . . . Davy Crockett was going on a manhunt, to find Black Bear.

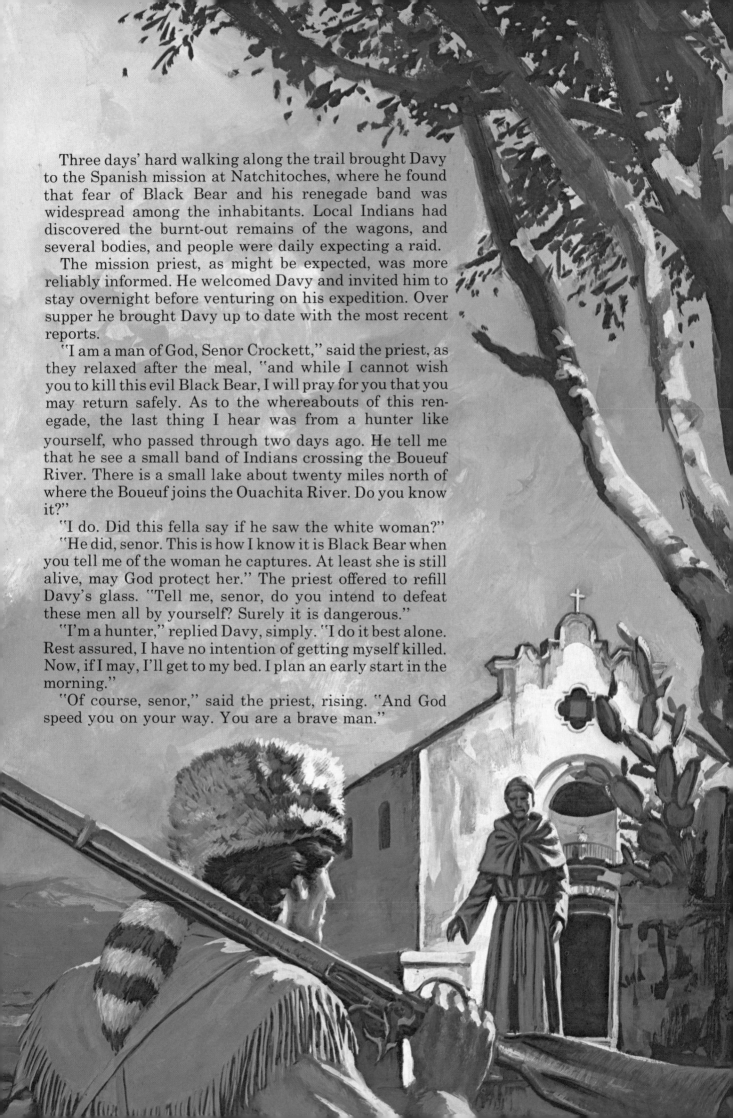

Three days' hard walking along the trail brought Davy to the Spanish mission at Natchitoches, where he found that fear of Black Bear and his renegade band was widespread among the inhabitants. Local Indians had discovered the burnt-out remains of the wagons, and several bodies, and people were daily expecting a raid.

The mission priest, as might be expected, was more reliably informed. He welcomed Davy and invited him to stay overnight before venturing on his expedition. Over supper he brought Davy up to date with the most recent reports.

"I am a man of God, Senor Crockett," said the priest, as they relaxed after the meal, "and while I cannot wish you to kill this evil Black Bear, I will pray for you that you may return safely. As to the whereabouts of this renegade, the last thing I hear was from a hunter like yourself, who passed through two days ago. He tell me that he see a small band of Indians crossing the Boueuf River. There is a small lake about twenty miles north of where the Boueuf joins the Ouachita River. Do you know it?"

"I do. Did this fella say if he saw the white woman?"

"He did, senor. This is how I know it is Black Bear when you tell me of the woman he captures. At least she is still alive, may God protect her." The priest offered to refill Davy's glass. "Tell me, senor, do you intend to defeat these men all by yourself? Surely it is dangerous."

"I'm a hunter," replied Davy, simply. "I do it best alone. Rest assured, I have no intention of getting myself killed. Now, if I may, I'll get to my bed. I plan an early start in the morning."

"Of course, senor," said the priest, rising. "And God speed you on your way. You are a brave man."

It is a difficult thing for an animal
that is used to being an all-powerful
hunter to adapt to the secret ways that
the hunted must adopt. So it was with
Black Bear and his band. Apart from
their unsuccessful skirmish the pre-
vious winter with Davy, they had suf-
fered no fatalities in their lightning
raids, and this unchecked progress had
made them grow disproportionately ar-
rogant of their strength and invinc-
ibility. While not openly inviting
attack, they had become less cautious
about covering their tracks, and once
Davy had closed the gap between them,
he found no difficulty in following their
trail.

For two weeks, once he had located
them, he followed their progress north
along the banks of the Mississippi,
biding his time, waiting his opportunity
to strike.

He had seen the white woman in the
camp, and while she was sometimes
treated rather roughly, there was no
danger of her being killed. Davy knew
he would, as always, be best served by
patience and vigilance. He had carefully observed their daily routine,
making a mental note of things that
particularly reoccurred, probing for a
weakness in their defences. It became

clear that Black Bear had a nightly practice of securing the woman to a tree, as soon as supper was over. While the braves sat round the fire and shared a pipe, there was little or no attention paid to the helpless captive. In this Davy saw his chance.

This particular night the campfire was set at a greater distance from the captive, thus providing Davy with the ideal opportunity to make his move. Waiting until darkness covered the woods, Davy made his way down to the bank of the river, and slipped silently into the shallow waters. He edged his way carefully along until he reached a point directly opposite the woman and, crawling on his stomach through the undergrowth, he slowly moved towards her, his senses acutely tuned to give warning of any sign of discovery.

She stood, head bowed forward as if in sleep, her long black hair cascading down over her shoulders, her long skirt billowing gently in the slight breeze. Holding his breath in, and hugging the shadows, Davy crept round to the rear of the tree.

"Don't make a sound," he whispered to her, "and we'll have you free in no time."

With a sudden whoop the figure pushed itself away from the tree, and Davy started in momentary horror as his gaze met the eyes of a Wichita warrior, his knife drawn. Within seconds the other braves were upon him, and he was dragged, struggling, to stand before Black Bear. In the firelight the Indian's cruel features looked demonic, an evil leer on his face.

"I see I baited the trap with the right meat," said Black Bear in the tongue of the Wichitas. "The great white hunter was completely fooled." His hand lashed out, knocking Davy to the ground. "I too am a hunter, white man, a greater one than you. Did you think I would have all my braves around me as we travelled, like so many cattle? No! Grey Hawk has been stalking you for three days—and now we have pounced on our prey."

Davy cursed himself silently for his oversight, one that could cost him his life. The Indian towered over him, looking down at his still form with a menacing glare.

"Bring the white woman to me," he bellowed. "She must see this."

Two braves immediately detached themselves from the group. Black Bear walked round the prone figure of Davy as he continued, the firelight flickering in his eyes.

"I could kill you with one blow," he said, slamming his fist into his palm, "but it is not a fitting end for a hunter. Instead we shall give you the chance that all animals have against the hunter—but first . . ." He paused, grinning at the expectant faces of the assembled braves. ". . . first we will make you run the gauntlet. You know, of course, of the old Indian custom? Should you survive you are free to try and make your escape, without weapons, you understand."

Davy understood all too well. The custom of running the gauntlet was one commonly used to test the bravery of warriors. Two rows of braves would form, a few feet apart, a narrow tunnel running between them. The warrior had to run down the middle while the braves rained blows on him with stones, clubs and tomahawks. Davy must first survive this test before he faced the challenge of being hunted down like an animal. It was not a pleasant prospect.

Within a matter of moments, two lines of armed warriors stood before him, their weapons threateningly poised to deal Davy his death blow. Regaining his breath, Davy steeled himself for the challenge, tensing his muscles with an iron determination. Black Bear's command broke through the still night air, and the test began.

Davy launched himself forward, feinting sharply to the right, his shoulder catching the first Indian a stunning blow in the midriff. Doubling up in pain, the brave crashed sideways into the next man, crucially disturbing the aim of the first two or three blows in the line. A tomahawk shaft glanced down across his back as Davy strode on, now veering to the left of the line, his arms chopping right and left, sending the weapons wildly astray.

A club caught him squarely on his side, knocking him off balance, and he fell to one knee. But, quickly taking advantage of the force of the blow, Davy flung himself at the legs of two warriors, toppling them, and continued his roll, narrowly missing the deadly sweep of a powerfully swung rock.

Drawing on all his agility he almost literally bounced to his feet, his legs levering away like pistons as he pushed aside the final warrior, a blade streaking past him, grazing his forehead. Almost as soon as it had begun the first ordeal was over and he had survived.

Ignoring the pain of his injuries he powered away into the trees, the disarrayed Indians slow to realise that he had miraculously escaped. Those vital seconds were what Davy needed. They gave him an invaluable head start of a few yards, for within seconds the first of the braves, led by Black Bear, surged after him, weapons held aloft.

To hunt an animal successfully one must know its ways, and be able to forecast accurately its given actions in any situation. Years of experience now repaid their value in full during those next, perilous minutes. The tricks of creatures that had escaped him and eluded capture now served Davy in a way he would always be thankful for. His diligence in learning the lessons of the hunter was never more valuable to him as he turned and swerved, creating first one false trail, then another, his delaying tactics all the time confusing and then gradually losing his pursuers one by one.

An hour later, exhausted and bleeding, Davy stopped
running. His breath came in fast, convulsive gasps as he
supported himself against a tree, his senses alert for any
further sounds of pursuit. There were none. He had faced
the toughest challenge of his life and lived. The knowledge strengthened him and his thoughts soon turned to
his incompleted task—the rescue of the white woman—
but this time he knew he must not fail.

The moon hung high and clear in the night sky as Davy
approached Black Bear's camp. The Indians had obviously abandoned the chase, for most of them lay
sleeping around the fading fire, although guards had
evidently been posted.

Davy was just pondering his best plan of attack when he saw one of the guards
drop to the ground like a stone, his heart transfixed by an arrow. Within
seconds, the clearing was alive with the cries of battle, as figures emerged from
the trees on all sides and fell upon the sleeping camp. It was a swift and ruthless
attack, against which Black Bear's braves were helpless. In the clear, moonlit
night they were easy targets.

Davy hesitated, watching from his position of cover. For an instant he saw the figure of Black Bear, unnoticed, slipping away towards the river. In a flash Davy was after him. He caught him at the water's edge, bringing the powerful Indian down with a lungeing dive. A blade flashed through the air, but Davy deflected the descending arm, smashing his other fist into his opponent's jaw. The renegade staggered backwards, stunned, and Davy leapt onto him, pinning him to the ground.

Black Bear's mystery assailants had by now caught sight of the struggle and one or two rushed over to help bring back the semi-conscious captive. As Davy followed them he caught sight of a distinctive figure held in the reflected light of the fire's dying embers. A long, healed scar on his thigh made it obvious that the man was none other than White Eagle. The battle between the two bands was all but over, and Davy entered the clearing to greet his old friend.

White Eagle, directing his braves to secure prisoners, recognised him at once and did not seem at all surprised to see him.

"It is good to see you still alive, white brother. I must confess to using you as a hunter would a deer."

Davy looked puzzled, but White Eagle continued, "For two days and two nights we have watched Black Bear, but I knew that he did not have all his braves with him. I could not attack before I knew the numbers of my enemy." The Indian smiled and put his arm round Davy's shoulder. "Yesterday, one of my braves saw you, and I knew you had come to rescue the white woman. I thought I would use you as bait to draw Black Bear's braves from the forest – forgive me, my brother, but it was the only way I could be sure."

Davy laughed. "I see you are a more cunning hunter than I am, White Eagle, and you have a fine catch to show for your skill."

The Indian shook his head. "It is you who have caught the bear; the honour of the hunt is yours."

The two men turned to survey the results of the attack. In one, well-planned raid White Eagle had rid the territory of an evil blight. Black Bear was brought struggling to stand before his victors. White Eagle withdrew the tomahawk from his belt and handed it to Davy.

"We have both hunted this murderer," he said simply, "but as his captor his life is forfeit to you alone. Do as you will."

Davy took the weapon, raised it above his head, and bringing the blade down with his full force, flung it into a tree trunk several feet behind the renegade. White Eagle looked shocked.

"It is not my way, White Eagle," explained Davy, silencing the Indian's protests. "You give him to me to do with as I will. Very well. Black Bear has murdered all who stood in his path, but it is not the white man's way to answer murder with murder. I seek not revenge, but justice, and with your help I shall take him back to Natchez to stand trial for his crimes. This is my will."

White Eagle nodded. "So be it, white brother. Your ways are strange, but as you honour the customs of my people so will I respect yours. It is a sign that our peoples should live in peace."

The white woman, shaken, but unhurt, accompanied by Davy, White Eagle and his braves, and the prisoners, returned to Natchez a few days later to a triumphant welcome.

Black Bear and his confederates were duly brought to trial and sentenced, and the lives of the settlers were again made safe from violent attack. Davy and White Eagle became blood brothers according to ancient Indian lore, and a celebration such as the town had never seen bound white brother to red brother in a bond of sacred trust.

Vengeance and justice both satisfied, White Eagle and his braves set out for their village. Davy too, though feted as a hero, longed for his solitude. Beckoned by the call of the wild, each, according to his nature, had once more returned to the backwoods, to the silence of the deep forests, and the pure unbounded energies of the great rivers.

With never a backward glance Davy was swallowed up by the vast, untamed tracts of that young yet ageless continent that was America. Answering the lure of nature, of man pitting his strength and wits in his struggle against the elements, Davy Crockett strode forward into the wilds, the hunter returning to his hunting grounds.

Though the man was gone, the memory of him remained. The days of Davy Crockett were to become legend wherever men strove to realise their greatness, and long after we are dead his deeds will burn strong and true in the hearts of men.